ADVANCED PROJECTS
FOR THE ELECTRIC GUITAR

Other Titles of Interest

ADVANCED PROJECTS
FOR THE ELECTRIC GUITAR

by

J. Chatwin

BERNARD BABANI (publishing) LTD
THE GRAMPIANS
SHEPHERDS BUSH ROAD
LONDON W6 7NF
ENGLAND

Please Note

Although every care has been taken with the production of this book to ensure that any projects, designs, modifications and/or programs, etc., contained herewith, operate in a correct and safe manner and also that any components specified are normally available in Great Britain, the Publishers do not accept responsibility in any way for the failure, including fault in design, of any project, design, modification or program to work correctly or to cause damage to any other equipment that it may be connected to or used in conjunction with, or in respect of any other damage or injury that may be so caused, nor do the Publishers accept responsibility in any way for the failure to obtain specified components.

Notice is also given that if equipment that is still under warranty is modified in any way or used or connected with home-built equipment then that warranty may be void.

© 1996 BERNARD BABANI (publishing) LTD

First Published – April 1996

British Library Cataloguing in Publication Data

Chatwin, J.

Advanced Projects for the Electric Guitar

I. Title

787.8719028

ISBN 0 85934 380 4

Printed and bound in Great Britain by Cox & Wyman Ltd, Reading

Preface

This book deals with electronic effects that can be used with the electric guitar, and other electronic instruments. These should be of interest to musicians as well as those into home recording and audio electronics. It contains a variety of projects, from simple mixers and single IC circuits, to relatively complex analogue and digital delay lines.

Some of the projects include complete PCB layouts and overlays, but due to the printing process, you should note that the absolute accuracy and dimensions of these can't be guaranteed. With others, the reader is left to design their own layouts, or to construct the projects in their own preferred way.

John Chatwin

Contents

Chapter 1

EFFECTS PEDALS

In this first section we will deal with a few of the most common and popular effects circuits that are used with electric guitars, and other electric instruments. In each example I've tried to make the circuits as complete as possible, to enable construction of working units that can simply be mounted in a suitable case, and plugged in without the need for extra circuitry or switches. In these basic arrangements, normal DPDT by-pass switches are indicated to bring the effects in and out. This form of double switching is very common, and works better – i.e. less noisily – than simply connecting or disconnecting one input or output with a single pole switch. DPDT foot switches are available for floor mounted effects, and it's probably a good idea to use one of these if a unit is going to get any sort of rough treatment. This is especially relevant if you play live, as fragile switches will undoubtedly fail just when you really need them to work. The section on electronic control has a couple of electronic by-pass circuits which may be connected in place of the heavy mechanical switches and triggered by single push-to-make switches. These might be better for making rack mounted or multiple effects units. They also make the wiring of an effect in/out LED indication easier.

In the majority of manufactured effects pedals, the overall power on/off is provided by using a stereo jack as a switch. When a normal mono jack plug is plugged in, the shaft shorts the first two terminals together connecting the negative feed from the battery to earth (Fig. 1.1). The only drawback with using this method is that you have to remember to pull out the plug at the end of a session or the battery will run down.

All of these effects circuits will operate from a standard PP3 9V battery, which means they should fit quite easily into small floor mounted effects cases.

It's best to try and use metal cases for guitar effects as they are not only stronger, they also provide screening, which is very important if noise levels are to be kept at a reasonable level.

1

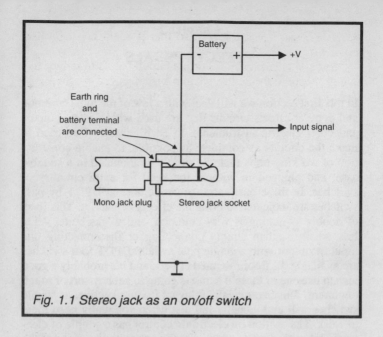

Fig. 1.1 Stereo jack as an on/off switch

Cases designed especially for mounting effects in are available, and are well worth investigating, as they may have battery compartments and pedal switches built in. A manufactured case might be quite expensive compared to the average project box, but will look a great deal more professional. This is especially true if you are going to construct a Wah Wah or volume pedal which needs to have moving parts.

Distortion Unit
Distortion has been around since the first attempts were made to amplify electric guitars. As the early experimenters were mostly jazz players who simply wanted to be heard clearly above a noisy load of sax and trumpets, distortion was – initially at least – something to be avoided.

With the coming of players who made a virtue of driving their amplifiers until the original guitar sound was virtually unrecognisable, came the need for circuitry to reproduce the

2

effect at lower volume levels, so that it could be controlled more easily.

The basic effect that a distortion circuit has, is to reduce the smoothly rounded guitar signal into a sharp edged square wave. The usual and most effective way of doing this is to make the input signal to an amplifier much greater than it can handle so that its output clips producing a rough edged and dirty sound. This works best in valve amplifiers for many – most subjective – reasons, but simple transistor circuits can produce perfectly adequate results.

The circuit shown in Figure 1.2 will produce two slightly different effects: a ragged dirty edged effect, and a severely distorted fuzz. IC1 is a low noise TL071 which amplifies the input signal and and feeds it to the input of IC2. The gain of this first stage amplifier is controlled by VR1, with R4 limiting its lowest setting to unity.

$$gain = R4 + VR1 / R1$$

Undistorted signals enter IC2 via coupling capacitor C3 and resistor R5. As noise levels are not particularly important in this stage, IC2 can be a general purpose 741. Another TL071 could be used if you wish.

IC2 is connected in the same way as IC1, with VR2 controlling the gain. The difference here is that diodes D2 and D3 connected across the feedback path act as limiters which clip the signal and create the characteristic distortion. The higher the gain setting, the more pronounced the effect, because at low gain only some signal peaks will be high enough to make the diodes forward conduct.

To keep out unwanted radio interference at high gain settings, C2 and C4 are included. C7 and C5 are decoupling capacitors, and if you are going to use an LED as a power indicator R7 acts as a current limiter. R2 and R3 provide a mid point voltage for both non-inverting inputs.

The circuit can be used to create the standard 'fuzzy' distortion, but will also provide enough clean output from IC1 to overdrive the input stages of most guitar amplifiers. The balance control VR3 is fed with both the clean and dirty signals so that a mix can be obtained at the output. Maximum distortion

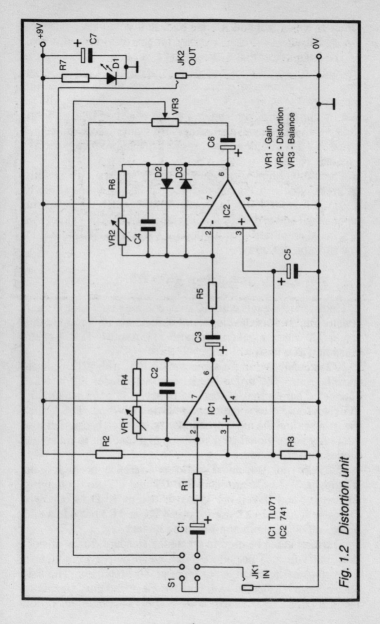

Fig. 1.2 Distortion unit

VR1 - Gain
VR2 - Distortion
VR3 - Balance

IC1 TL071
IC2 741

4

will occur when IC1 and IC2 are both full on.

A PCB and component overlay for the distortion unit are shown in Figures 1.3 and 1.4

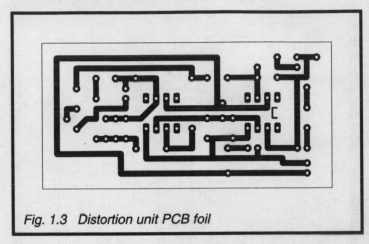

Fig. 1.3 Distortion unit PCB foil

Components for Distortion Unit (Fig.1.2)

Resistors (all 0.25 watt 5% carbon film)
R1, R2, R3, R4   47k (4 off)
R5, R6   22k (2 off)
R7   1k
VR1, VR2   1M log potentiometers (2 off)
VR3   1M lin potentiometer

Capacitors
C1, C3, C6   1µF 16V electrolytic (3 off)
C2, C4   68pF ceramic (2 off)
C5   10µF 16V electrolytic
C7   100µF 16V electrolytic

Semiconductors
IC1   TL071
IC2   741
D1   LED
D2, D3   OA91 germanium diode (2 off)

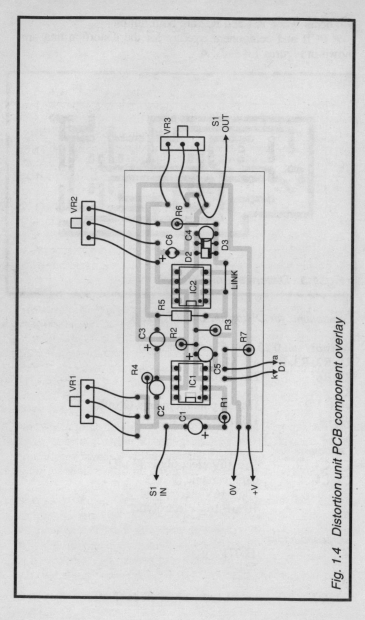

Fig. 1.4 Distortion unit PCB component overlay

Miscellaneous

JK1, JK2   ¼ inch mono jack sockets (2 off)

S1   DPDT switch

Tremolo

Tremolo is quite an old and basic effect used a lot in the 50s and 60s. It went out of fashion with the advent of chorus and flanging, but seems to be gaining popularity again. Tremolo circuits are often found in valve amps like the Vox AC30, or the Fender twin reverb. More recently they have appeared in transistor amplifiers as a bit of extra gimmickry.

Tremolo is simply a form of amplitude modulation that can produce an effect similar to a repeating echo. Unfortunately most people over-do it when they use a tremolo and it tends to become a bit of a joke. To use a tremolo creatively requires a bit of patience, and careful attention to the depth and rate controls. It can be very effective if treated subtly.

There is often some confusion over the difference between tremolo and vibrato. This may have arisen over the misnaming of the guitar 'trem', and the term 'vibtrem' given to some tremolo circuits. The tremolo arm on a guitar actually produces a vibrato, or modulation of the frequency, not tremolo, which is modulation of the amplitude. A true vibrato circuit that modulates the frequency of a signal can be built using the analogue delay line described later.

The tremolo circuit shown here (Fig. 1.5) is relatively simple, yet can give good results with a variety of other instruments, as well as the electric guitar. It consists of two main parts, a variable gain amplifier, and a low frequency oscillator which controls it via an isolator made up from a light emitting diode (LED) and a light dependent resistor (LDR).

The control oscillator is a conventional square wave type built from a 4011 quad NAND gate (IC1). VR1 and C3 control the frequency of the oscillator, and with these components its range is from 2Hz to around 9Hz. This gives a good usable fast and slow effect. If you want the oscillator to go faster than this you can reduce the value of R1 or C3. For a slower effect, make R1 or C3 bigger.

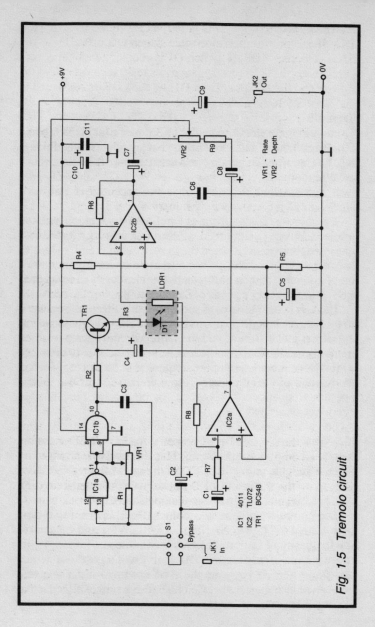

Fig. 1.5 Tremolo circuit

8

The output from the LFO is fed via R2 to the base of TR1. This transistor acts as an electronic switch that turns D1 on and off in response to the oscillator. D1 is coupled to a light dependent resistor LDR1, which changes its resistance depending on the level of light coming from D1. As the LDR is connected to the input of IC2(b), the gain of this section depends on its value. In complete darkness, the LDR has a very high resistance – something around 2 to 3M – while this falls to 1k or so with D1 full on. This means that signals passing through IC2(b) are turned on and off at a rate dependent on the control oscillator.

IC2(a) is wired as a standard inverting amplifier and feeds an unmodulated version of the input signal through to VR2. This pot acts as a depth control by allowing a variable amount of the modulated output from IC2(b) to be mixed with the output from IC1(a).

As the circuit has an oscillator that produces square waves, it is important that the power rails are adequately decoupled to stop noise spikes appearing at the output. Having the oscillator isolated by the LDR helps to reduce noise quite a lot because it has a relatively slow response time, but unless the decoupling capacitors C4, C5, C6, C10 and C11 are included, noise may be a problem. C11 should be mounted close to IC1. It is advisable to keep all connections to the oscillator as short as possible, and if you can, position it away from the other sections of the circuit.

LDR

To enable the circuit to work properly, the LDR/LED assembly has to be completely light-proof. This can easily be arranged by using superglue to join the LED to the top of the resistor, after first filing the top of the LED flat to make a better joint (Fig. 1.6). The whole assembly can then be coated in black paint to stop any ambient light getting to the LDR. This is not so important if the circuit is going into a light-proof case, but makes testing easier under normal lighting conditions.

The type of LED and LDR that you use are not vitally important, virtually any combination should work. The prototype that this circuit is based on had a large 5mm LED glued to the top of an ORP12 LDR.

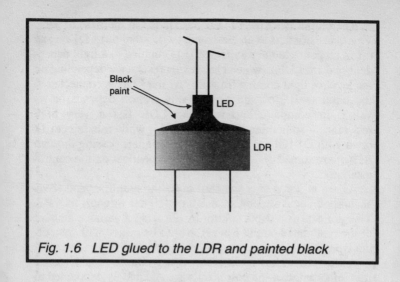

Fig. 1.6 LED glued to the LDR and painted black

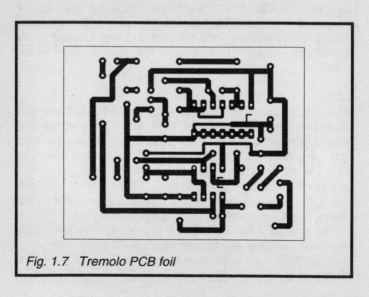

Fig. 1.7 Tremolo PCB foil

10

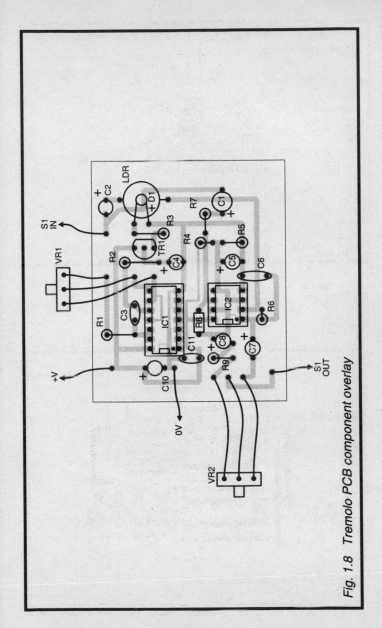

Fig. 1.8 Tremolo PCB component overlay

11

Figures 1.7 and 1.8 show a PCB and component overlay for the tremolo circuit.

Components for Tremolo Circuit (Fig. 1.5)

Resistors (all 0.25 watt 5% carbon film)
R1	820k
R2	470R
R3, R7	1k (2 off)
R4, R5	100k (2 off)
R6	47k
R8	10k
R9	15k
VR1	2M2 lin
VR2	100k lin
LDR1	ORP12 light-dependent resistor

Capacitors
C1, C2, C7, C8, C9	1µF 16V electrolytic (5 off)
C3, C11	100nF polyester
C4	22µF 16V electrolytic
C5	10µF 16V electrolytic
C6	22nF polyester
C10	100µF 16V electrolytic

Semiconductors
IC1	4011
IC2	TL072
TR1	BC547
D1	5mm LED

Miscellaneous
JK1, JK2	¼ inch mono jack sockets (2 off)
S1	DPDT switch

Hall Effect Volume Pedal
A volume pedal can be a highly effective piece of equipment. You can use it to create violining and other sounds that need a

slow attack and it's especially effective connected at the end of an effects chain, or after a distortion unit. The usual way to fade notes in and out is to have the little finger of your strumming hand operate the volume knob while you play. This can sound great, but needs a lot of practice and may be difficult if the volume control on your guitar is well away from where you normally have your hand. Using a volume pedal can free you up to do fancy fingering techniques with both hands at the same time, while controlling the volume with your foot. A volume pedal is also good for simply controlling the overall output from a line of effects which you may not want to run flat out all the time, feeding noise into your amplifier.

The circuit in Figure 1.9 is relatively complicated if you consider that simply having a potentiometer connected to some form of pedal arrangement would probably work just as well. The mechanical option has a couple of disadvantages though. The first is that if you don't have an old pedal that you can adapt for the job, you will have to build a mechanism that smoothly operates a mechanical potentiometer when you push down on it with your foot – this is actually quite difficult unless you don't mind playing in front of people with a lash up of ratchets and wire strapped to your foot.

The other disadvantage is noise. Even top quality potentiometers will end up sounding rough after a few weeks of being knocked around close to the floor, and this can make the effect unusable.

The volume pedal circuit shown here is magnetically controlled and uses a Hall Effect sensor to alter the gain of an op-amp through which the instrument signal passes. This is a common way of doing things in expensive manufactured pedals, though a basic circuit like this is cheap to build and works very well, with virtually silent operation.

A Hall Effect sensor is a magnetically sensitive semiconductor that produces an output current proportional to the strength of a local magnetic field, so the only mechanical requirement of a suitable pedal is that it brings a small magnet closer to the sensor when you put your foot on it. This makes construction a bit more realistic, though you will need to experiment to find the best place to put the sensor in relation to the magnet. I found that only a small amount of movement was

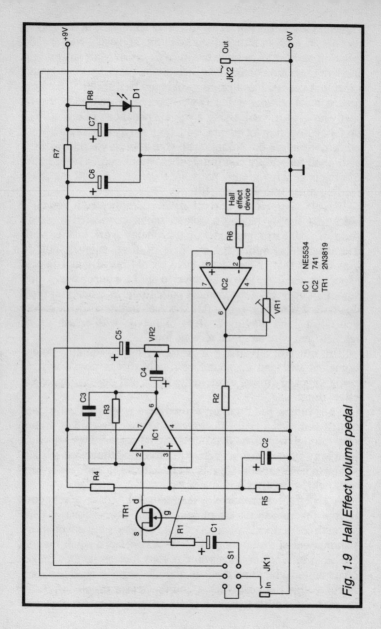

Fig. 1.9 Hall Effect volume pedal

IC1 NE5534
IC2 741
TR1 2N3819

14

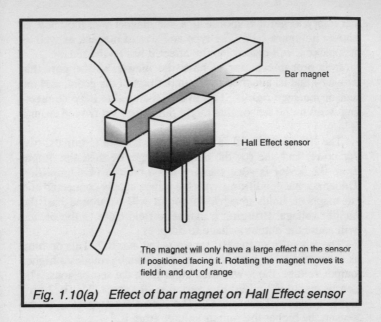

The magnet will only have a large effect on the sensor if positioned facing it. Rotating the magnet moves its field in and out of range

Fig. 1.10(a)   Effect of bar magnet on Hall Effect sensor

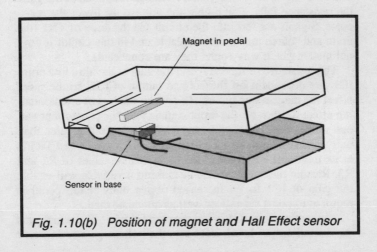

Fig. 1.10(b)   Position of magnet and Hall Effect sensor

necessary to get a response if a bar magnet was mounted as shown in Figure 1.10. The type and size of magnet, as well as its position, will determine the affect it has on the sensor.

It is probably better to have the magnet as the part that moves – that is, attached to the upper part of the pedal, and the sensor mounted rigidly. This avoids the need to have connecting wires to the sensor that might fail if they get moved around a lot.

The HE sensor used in this circuit has three terminals, two for power and one for the output voltage. Because the output from the device is very small, it has a built-in FET amplifier. Under normal conditions, with the power supply connected and no magnetic fields nearby, its output will be around half the supply voltage. Bringing a magnetic field close to the device will cause the output voltage to drop.

The output from the HE sensor is fed into IC2. This op-amp is connected as an inverting amplifier which provides a higher output voltage, the lower the output from the sensor goes. The sensor output is limited to a variation of approx. 1V. IC2 produces a swing of around 4V. The closer the magnet is to the sensor, the higher the output voltage from IC2.

The main control element in the circuit is the FET, TR1. Under normal conditions the resistance between the drain and source is extremely high. When a voltage is applied to the gate, the resistance falls. The higher the voltage the lower the resistance. Signals are fed into the circuit via the drain of TR1 (the drain and source are interchangeable and in this circuit it does not matter which way round they are connected).

The resistance of the FET, and the gain of the ultra low noise IC1, are dependent on the voltage output of IC2, so the more effect the magnet has on the HE sensor, the less of an attenuating effect IC1 has on the input signal. With the component values shown here, IC1 will never have an output greater than unity, and still has a slight attenuating action even when TR1 is at its minimum resistance, due to the equal values of R1 and R3. Raising the value of R3, or making it variable will enable the gain of IC1 to be increased above unity if the pedal is required to boost signals as well as attenuate them.

The output from IC1 is fed through C4 into VR2, which sets the overall output level. VR1 sets the voltage gain of IC2 and can be used to trim the sensitivity of the control circuit.

Because the Hall Effect sensor has a maximum working voltage of 8V, R7 needs to be included to drop the supply down to a safe level. C6 and C7 are the usual smoothing capacitors, with S1 as a by-pass switch.

A PCB and component overlay for the volume pedal are shown in Figures 1.11 and 1.12.

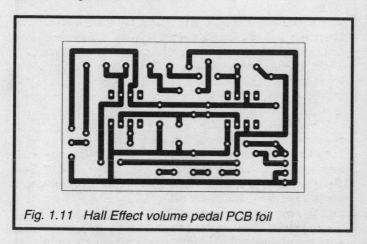

Fig. 1.11   Hall Effect volume pedal PCB foil

Components for Hall Effect Volume Pedal (Fig. 1.9)

Resistors (all 0.25 watt 5% carbon film)

R1	22k
R2	2M2
R3	22k
R4, R5	10k (2 off)
R6	5k6
R7	150R
R8	1k
VR1	240k preset
VR2	470k log potentiometer

Capacitors

C1, C4, C5	1µF 16V electrolytic (3 off)
C2, C6	10µF 16V electrolytic

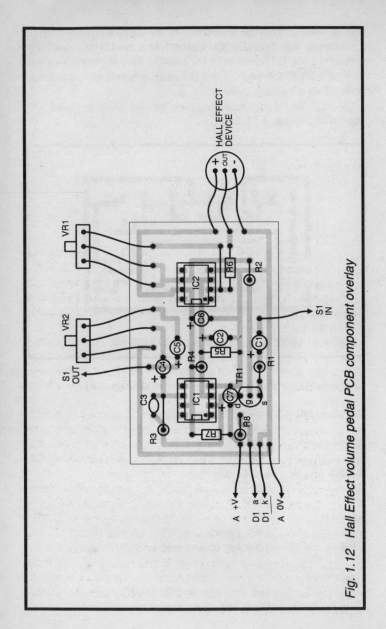

Fig. 1.12 Hall Effect volume pedal PCB component overlay

18

| C3 | 180pF ceramic |
| C7 | 100µF 16V electrolytic |

Semiconductors

IC1	NE5534
IC2	741
TR1	2N3819
D1	3mm LED
	Hall Effect Sensor UGN3503U

Miscellaneous

| JK1, JK2 | ¼ inch mono jack sockets (2 off) |
| S1 | DPDT switch |

Hall Effect Wah Wah

Another effect that can take advantage of the Hall Effect is Wah Wah. This is created by manually sweeping a band pass filter up and down the audio spectrum. As with volume pedals, this is often done by connecting a potentiometer mechanically to a pedal. But doing this brings the same disadvantages of complexity and noisy operation.

In this Wah Wah circuit (Fig. 1.13) the Hall Effect sensor controls a FET in the same way as in the volume pedal except that in this case, instead of controlling the gain of an op-amp, the variable resistance shifts the resonant frequency of a band pass filter.

Input signals from J1 are amplified by IC1 which gives them the necessary level to feed the filter effectively. If required, the gain of IC1 can be increased by raising the value of R4 so that it overdrives the filter, which can produce some interesting distortion effects.

The filter is a conventional band pass arrangement, based around the feedback path of low noise IC2. Capacitors C6 and C5 determine the filters resonant frequency, along with VR1 and the source/drain resistance of TR1. In this circuit C5 and C6 are 100nF giving the filter a good effective range for the average electric guitar. It may be worthwhile experimenting with other values for the capacitors to get an effect that suits you. The output from IC2 feeds into VR2 so that the overall volume of the effect can be adjusted.

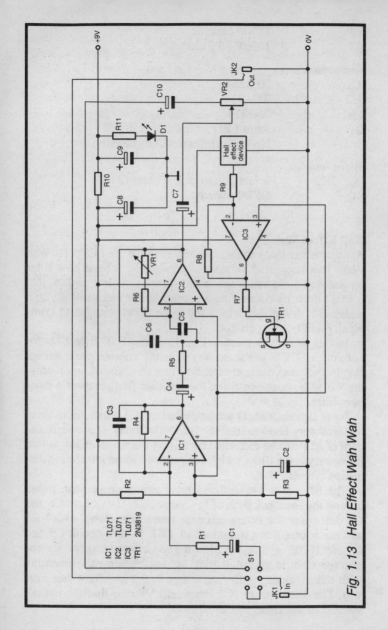

Fig. 1.13 Hall Effect Wah Wah

20

The filter control operates in a similar way to the control circuit for the volume pedal. An output voltage from the Hall Effect sensor is amplified by IC3 and used to control TR1. With a magnet close to the sensor the resistance of the FET is high, and the filter has little effect on incoming signals. As the magnetic field close to the sensor decreases, the voltage from IC3 increases, and the source/drain resistance of TR1 falls. This produces the familiar Wah Wah effect. The potentiometer VR1 can be used as a range control to determine where the limit of the sweep will be. This pot can be a preset type if it isn't going to be used a great deal.

As with the volume pedal, the supply to the Hall Effect sensor needs to be no more than 8V, so R10 is included to enable a standard PP3 battery to be connected. If different batteries are to be used, four 1.5V cells for instance, R10 can be omitted.

Using the Wah Wah is very straightforward, assuming that you can get a suitable pedal together that will bring a magnet close to the sensor. If you want to use it with a potentiometer arrangement, simply leave out the Hall Effect sensor and IC3, and connect a 100k lin potentiometer in place of TR1.

Figures 1.14 and 1.15 are a PCB layout and component overlay for the Wah Wah.

Components for Hall Effect Wah Wah (Fig. 1.13)

Resistors (all 0.25 watt 5% carbon film)

R1, R6	22k (2 off)
R2, R3, R4	100k (3 off)
R5, R7, R11	1k (3 off)
R8	47k
R9	6k8
R10	150R
VR1	1M lin pot
VR2	470k log pot

Capacitors

C1, C4, C7, C10	10µF 16V electrolytic (4 off)
C2, C8	22µF 16V electrolytic (2 off)
C3	180pF
C5, C6	100nF polyester (2 off)
C9	220µF 16V electrolytic

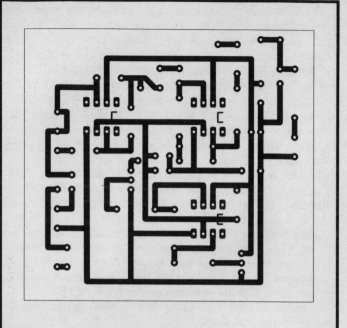

Fig. 1.14 Hall Effect wah wah PCB foil

Semiconductors

IC1, IC2, IC3	TL071 (3 off)
D1	3mm LED
TR1	2N3819
	Hall Effect sensor UGN3503U

Miscellaneous

JK1, JK2	¼ inch mono jack sockets (2 off)
S1	DPDT switch

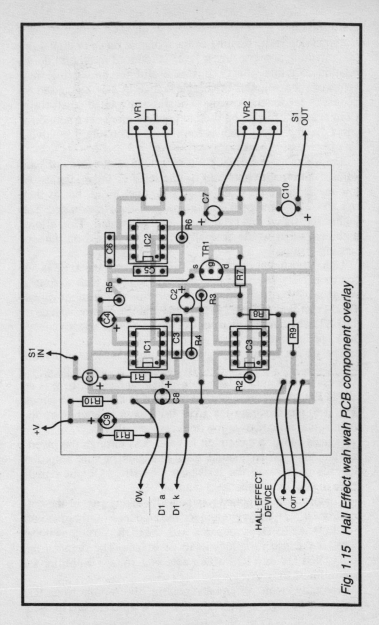

Fig. 1.15 Hall Effect wah wah PCB component overlay

Compressor

Compression is the limiting of the dynamic range of signals so that anything above a preset level is reduced in amplitude. In relation to guitar effects, this is useful for preventing high peaks or sudden jumps in volume – such as may be caused by acoustic feedback – from causing unwanted distortion. Compressors can also be used to create a more even sound for some playing styles, such as funk bass, which might involve a lot of percussive peaks.

Compressors are usually based around some form of gain adjustment circuit controlled by the level of input signals. At low levels the input signals may pass unchanged, but as they rise above a preset level they are progressively attenuated. The higher the signal level the more it is attenuated. This allows high peaks that would normally clip to be passed on without causing distortion.

Gain adjustment can be achieved in several ways. FETs are commonly employed as the variable element, with a control voltage derived from an amplified version of the input signal. This is rectified and used to alter the drain/source resistance of the FET, which might then control the amount of negative feedback applied to the original signal.

The circuit shown in Figure 1.16 uses an older and more basic method, but one that is still popular because of its effectiveness and simplicity. The gain adjusting element here is an LDR/LED arrangement like the one used in the Tremolo circuit (Fig. 1.5). In this case the LED brightness is altered by the input signal instead of a low frequency oscillator.

Signals entering the circuit have to pass through the inverting amplifier based around IC1. The gain of this amplifier depends on R3 and the resistance of LDR1. Output signals leave the circuit via the level control VR1.

Compression is applied to signals by taking part of the output from IC1 and using it to vary the amount of light given off by LED1. As LED1 is mounted with the LDR, variations in the light level cause variations in its resistance. The output from IC1 is first fed into IC2 which acts as a voltage amplifier for controlling LED1.

Normally, with no signals present, the output from IC2 should not be high enough to light LED1, which means the gain

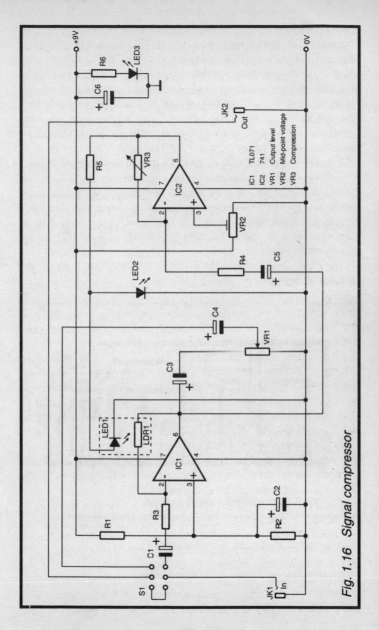

Fig. 1.16 Signal compressor

25

of IC1, and the output of the circuit are very high. For regular operation the compressor needs to have a relatively low gain, so VR3 is used to set the standby voltage to LED1 until the gain of IC1 is brought down to the required level. VR2 can also be used to adjust IC2 for standby conditions but should be set initially so that the voltage to pin 3 of IC2 is approximately half the supply. LED2 is useful for setting up the circuit as you can use it to judge the level of LED1. Initially VR3 should be adjusted until you can just see LED2 light. VR1 can then be utilised to match the output level to that of the original input.

When operating normally, the compressor will have no effect on signals passing through it that are below the threshold level set by VR3. As soon as anything above the threshold appears, the output of IC2 makes LED1 brighter which reduces the resistance of the LDR, and brings the gain of IC1 down, compressing the signal.

A PCB and component overlay for the compressor are shown in Figures 1.17 and 1.18.

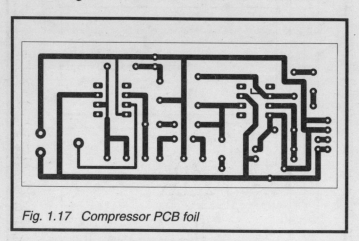

Fig. 1.17   Compressor PCB foil

Components for Signal Compressor (Fig. 1.16)

Resistors (all 0.25 watt 5% carbon film)
R1, R2   10k
R3   47k

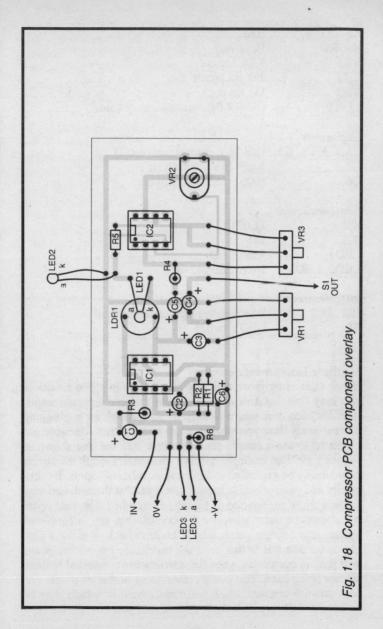

Fig. 1.18 Compressor PCB component overlay

R4	100k
R5, R6	1k (2 off)
VR1	470k log pot
VR2	25k lin preset
VR3	1M lin pot
LDR1	ORP12 light-dependent resistor

Capacitors
C1, C3, C4, C5	1µF 16V electrolytic (4 off)
C2	10µF 16V electrolytic
C6	100µF 16V electrolytic

Semiconductors
IC1	TL071
IC2	741
LED1	5mm LED
LED2, LED3	3mm LEDs (2 off)

Miscellaneous
| JK1, JK2 | ¼ inch mono jack sockets (2 off) |
| S1 | DPDT switch |

Multiple Instrument Selector

If you start using more than one instrument in a live situation, you may find that unless you are able to have separate amplifiers for each one, you will have to go through an unplugging routine every time you want to swap instruments. One solution might be to use a simple passive mixer like the one shown in Figure 1.19. This example has four channels, though the circuit could easily be expanded to have any number of inputs. Its simplicity and passive action means that it is a bit limited, and may cause a slight attenuation of signals, even when it is wide open, but should be quite adequate for combining, say, a couple of guitars into a single guitar amp. One drawback of using a simple mixer like this is that once the levels are set, all the inputs will remain open even when the instruments connected to them are not being used. This could create noise problems unless you turn down a channel when you finish with it, which may be awkward if the preset level is critical and you are in a hurry.

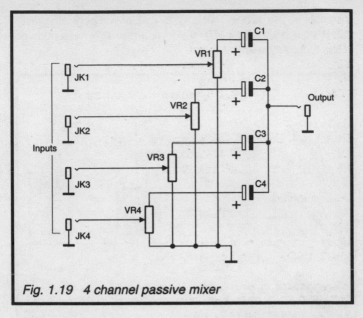

Fig. 1.19   4 channel passive mixer

The circuit shown in Figure 1.21 is an electronic channel selector which will take up to four different instruments, and switch any one of them electronically to a single output. The aim of this is to simplify things a little on stage, when fiddling with sliders or potentiometers can be a bit of a distraction. The unit simply allows you to select the input that goes to your amplifier by stamping on a single SPDT foot-switch, which you can do while you swap instruments, saving time and making you look more professional. The preset levels of each instrument can be selected beforehand at a sound check, then left alone. All you need to do is make sure the correct channel indicator LED is lit (Fig. 1.21).

The channel selector is very simple to make, requiring only a couple of ICs and a few other bits to get it going. It has an advantage in being electronically controlled in that a single selector switch can be used to sequence through the channels. The most important points of construction are the case and the foot-switch. Both of these should be as rugged as possible, as they are likely to get a lot of physical abuse. This won't matter so much if you are a gentle type and never play anywhere except your bedroom, but then you will probably have no need of the thing any way.

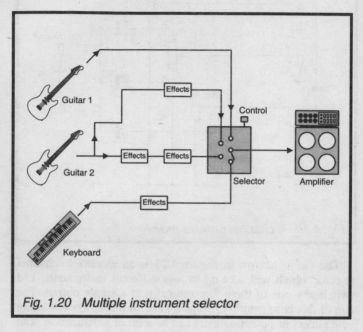

Fig. 1.20 Multiple instrument selector

The circuit for the channel selector is based around half of an LM1037 dual 4 channel analogue switch. This IC has eight electronically controlled switches split into two groups of four. Each set of four channels has a common output, and taking the relevant control pin high will route one of the four channels to it (Fig. 1.22). The 1037 is really intended for applications such as stereo source selection, and as such, has extremely good channel isolation as well as a click free operation.

As the object of the selector is simplicity of operation, the switch selector inputs of the 1037 are controlled by a manually clocked ripple counter formed around IC1. This is a well known and versatile 4017 which will send one of its ten outputs high every time a clock pulse is detected on pin 14. In this case we only want it to cycle through the first four of its outputs,

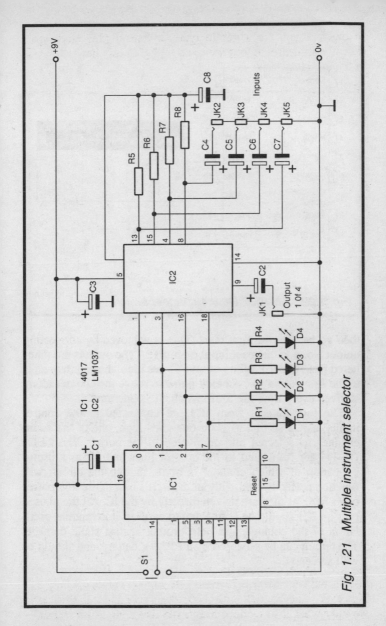

Fig. 1.21 Multiple instrument selector

31

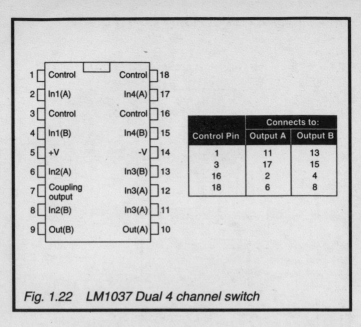

Fig. 1.22 LM1037 Dual 4 channel switch

then go back to the first one. This is achieved by connecting output No. 4 to the reset input on pin 15. (The outputs are numbered from 0 to 9.) When output 4 goes high, the counter resets to the first output '0'. A clock pulse to move the counter along is given every time the foot-switch S1 is operated.

The four outputs from IC1 are connected to the control inputs of IC2 so that as each one goes high, one of the audio channels is selected and connected to the output. The LEDs D1–D4 are connected to the control lines and act as a useful indication of which channel is open, though the circuit will function perfectly well without them. It's best to use low power types here, as they are driven directly by the IC. All the unused pins on IC1 should be connected to earth to stop random oscillation of the counter, and help protect against static damage. The circuit can be powered by a PP3 9V battery, and should be well screened.

Components for 4-Channel Passive Mixer (Fig. 1.19)

Resistors
VR1 – VR4   100k log potentiometers (4 off)

Capacitors
C1 – C4   1µF 16V electrolytic (4 off)

Miscellaneous
JK1 – JK5   ¼ inch mono jack sockets (5 off)

Components for Multiple Instrument Selector (Fig. 1.21)

Resistors (all 0.25 watt 5% carbon film)
R1 – R4   1k (4 off)
R5 – R8   100k (4 off)

Capacitors
C1, C3   10µF 16V electrolytic (2 off)
C2, C4, C5,   1µF 16V tantalum bead (5 off)
C6, C7
C8   100µF 16V electrolytic

Semiconductors
IC1   4017
IC2   LM1037
D1 – D4   3mm LEDs (4 off)

Miscellaneous
JK1 – JK5   ¼ inch mono jack sockets (2 off)
S1   SPDT switch

Chapter 2

DELAY LINES

Nowadays, audio delay lines are used extensively in music processing, not only to create simple echo and reverberation, but a whole range of other effects. These include chorus, flanging, double tracking, frequency shifting, etc., and often involve modulation of the delay time.

In the past, the only realistic delay units relied on loops of recording tape being passed over two or more recording heads. The first head would record a signal onto the tape, and the second head would play the signal back (Fig. 2.1). The delay time depended on the distance between the heads and the speed of the tape. Commercial echo machines, like the well known 'Watkins Copycat' had four 0.25″ mono play-back heads spaced out along the tape, followed by an erase head at the end of the line. The erase head needed to be there to clean off the tape before more information was recorded onto the loop. Disconnecting the erase head was a popular modification

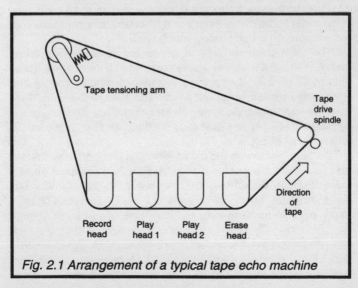

Fig. 2.1 Arrangement of a typical tape echo machine

which allowed the machine to function as a continuous tape loop, with signals constantly repeating every time they passed a play-back head. A big drawback with most tape echo machines was the relatively poor sound reproduction and frequency response. This was due in part to the quality of the recording heads, the tape transport mechanism, and the size of the tape loop.

In machines like the 'Copycat', the tape loop was only around 60cm long, and revolved at quite a high speed. This meant that even with high quality tape, the constant rubbing on the tape heads soon wore it out, resulting in a loss of sound quality. Tape loops were also liable to snap, usually at the point where they were spliced together.

Higher quality tape echo machines had much longer tape loops and better heads to cut down on tape wear. In recording studios, normal multiple head tape machines could be used to give the highest quality echo effects.

Reverberation
The creation of reverberation is somewhat simpler than making longer echoes. Reverberation is used to enhance sounds by making them seem to be in a larger space than they really are. This could be anything from a small 'bright' environment, like a bathroom, to a vast spacey concert hall.

The most common way of producing reverberation, even today, is to use a long thin spring suspended between two transducers (Fig. 2.2). Signals are introduced at one end of the spring and picked up at the other. The time delay caused by their passage along the spring creates the effect. The longer the spring the deeper the reverb. Feedback is also provided to enhance the effect.

Because of the way the sound vibrations reflect up and down the spring decaying away slowly, this method produces quite a natural effect. Virtually all the reverb units found in guitar and instrument amplifiers use this method. Spring lines can be anything from 20 to 30cm long and may have two or more springs mounted side by side to enhance the effect. Other ways to create reverb have been used in recording, such as suspending large metal sheets in a room with a microphone on one side and speaker on the other. Sounds from the speaker cause the metal

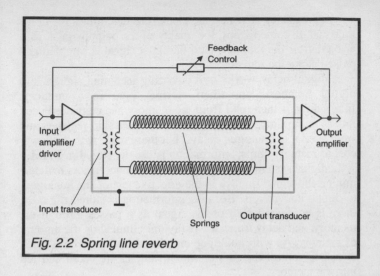

Fig. 2.2 Spring line reverb

sheets to reverberate and this is picked up by the microphone. Methods like this have been made obsolete by the availability of high quality electronic effects.

Electronic Delay Lines

With the advances in semiconductor technology that have occurred over the last 15 years or so, it is now much easier to create echo and reverberation effects in a purely electronic way, thus avoiding the drawbacks of devices that use mechanical and moving parts. There are two main types of electronic delay – Analogue and Digital.

Analogue delays are the simpler of the two and use tiny capacitors to store samples of charge relating to an input signal. These charges are then passed along some form of shift register which is driven by a timing circuit or clock. This system is sometimes called a 'bucket brigade' or BBD, and has the advantage of being relatively cheap, but is realistically limited to short delays and effects that require no more than 50–100ms or so because of the signal degradation that occurs as information is passed down the register. A typical BBD chip might have around 500 or 1000 stages, and require an external clock to run the shift register.

37

The frequency at which the clock runs determines the delay time and, to some extent, the quality of the output signal, as it also controls the rate at which the input signal is sampled and passed along the register.

A digital delay works by converting incoming signals into digital numbers, and then storing them in a memory. Information is then read from the memory and converted back into an audio signal. Early digital delays used shift registers and were similar to analogue delays, but these days, with the lower cost of memory chips, information is usually stored in RAM.

In digital systems, one of the most important factors in determining the signal quality is the effectiveness of the analogue-to-digital conversion. Because information is stored digitally, there is no degradation of the signal as it passes through the memory, and delay times are really only limited by the amount of memory. As with analogue circuits, there has to be a clock circuit to control the rate at which samples are taken and fed into the memory.

Sampling

To convert an audio signal into a form that can be processed by a delay circuit, it has to be sampled at regular intervals and its amplitude recorded. In an analogue delay a single sample will correspond to an amount of charge on a capacitor. In a digital circuit a sample will be converted into a digital number. The rate at which samples are taken is important if a signal is to be reproduced with any accuracy, and in general, the lowest usable rate is regarded as having to be at least twice the maximum frequency being sampled. This means that to process audio signals, which have an upper limit of around 20kHz, a sampling rate of 40kHz should be required. In practice, much lower rates can be used because most audio and music occurs in the low and middle frequency ranges. Logarithmically scaled converters may be used to take samples that are more defined in the mid range and become progressively less so as the frequency increases. Figure 2.3 shows how a part of an audio signal is sampled.

To enable the sampling circuitry to operate with maximum efficiency, digital samplers often include a 'hold' circuit synchronised to the analogue-to-digital converter. This works by keeping the input to the converter at a constant level for the time it takes to make one sample, allowing the usable range of the circuit to be improved by ensuring that an accurate conversion takes place each time a sample is taken, which might not be the case if the input is fluctuating rapidly or has a very high frequency content.

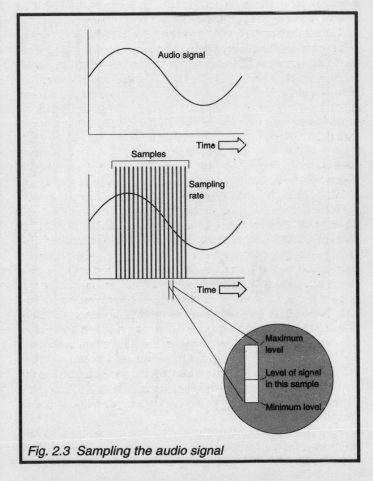

Fig. 2.3 Sampling the audio signal

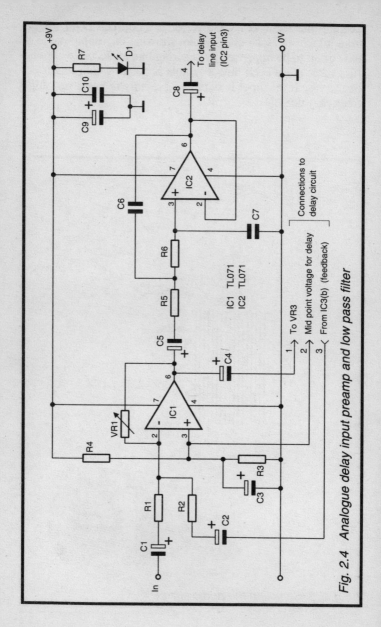

Fig. 2.4 Analogue delay input preamp and low pass filter

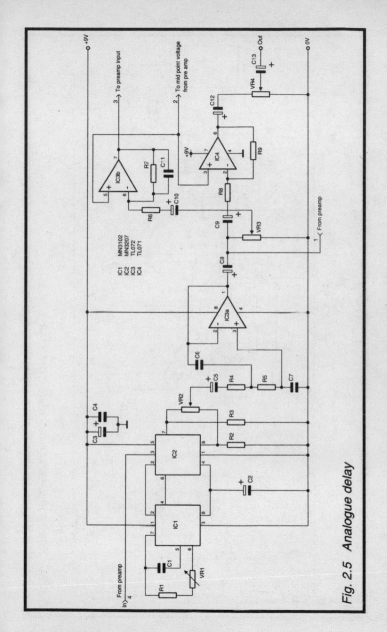

Fig. 2.5 Analogue delay

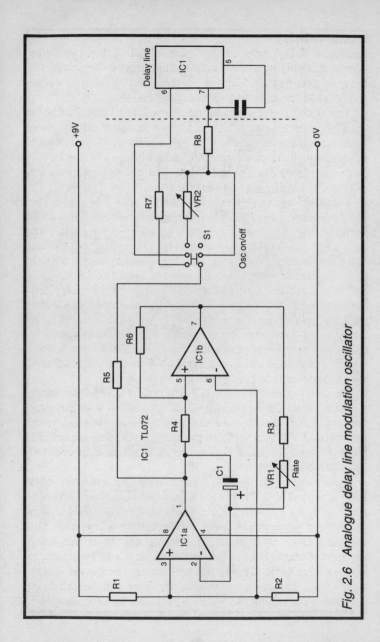

Fig. 2.6 Analogue delay line modulation oscillator

42

Analogue Delay

Analogue delay lines can be very effective for producing effects that only need short delays, though once the delay time required gets beyond 50ms or so, they tend to become a little too noisy for realistic use in audio applications.

The analogue delay shown in Figures 2.4, 2.5 and 2.6 can be used to create several effects, including chorus, flanging, short echo and basic reverb. For the echo effects that don't require modulation, there is no need to include the oscillator circuit shown in Figure 2.6. This will be needed if you want to use the circuit for flanging and chorus effects.

The basic analogue delay line is split into two parts. The input circuitry, and the delay line itself. Figure 2.4 consists of an input preamp/mixer followed by an active low-pass filter with a cut off point at around 15kHz. The mixer/preamp and filter are based around two TL071 low noise op-amps. Signals enter the circuit via C1 and R1 and are amplified by IC1. C2 and R2 introduce signals from the output of the delay line circuitry to enable feedback effects to be produced. VR1 controls the gain of the mixer. The output from this section feeds into the low-pass filter formed around IC2. C4 is connected to the output of the delay circuit (connection point 1) and feeds a 'straight' signal to the output circuitry allowing a mix of both the 'straight' and delayed signals to be produced.

The mid point voltage for IC1 is given by R3 and R4, along with the decoupling capacitor C3. IC3(b) and IC4 in the main delay circuit (Fig. 2.5) also share this voltage via connection point No. 2. C9 and C10 are the main smoothing capacitors, while R7 and the LED D1 can be included as a 'power on' indicator if required.

From the output of IC1, signals enter the low-pass filter formed around IC2. This is a standard two pole active arrangement with its cut off frequency set at around 15kHz. This means that frequencies above 15kHz will be attenuated. The low-pass filter is included to remove any high frequency signals before they get to the delay line, as it will be unable to process them correctly, and this will increase noise and distortion levels. The cut off level for the filter can be raised or lowered by changing the values of R5 and R6 or C6 and C7. For this type of circuit both of the resistors and both of the capacitors need to be of the same value. The formula for calculating the cut off frequency is:

$$R = 0.16 / C \times Fc$$

For example, to make a 15kHz filter with 1nF capacitors:

$$C = 1nF = 1 \times 10^{-9}$$

$$15000 \times 1 \times 10^{-9} = 0.000015$$

$$0.16 / 0.000015 = 10666$$

$$R = 10666$$

The nearest value resistor to 10666R in the E12 series is 10k, and this will do fine for this filter, as the cut off frequency is not critical.

From the output of IC 2 in the preamp circuit, signals are sent to the input of the delay line (Fig. 2.5). This circuit consists of a 1024 stage low voltage BBD IC (IC1), a clock generator (IC2), and output circuitry including an active low-pass filter like the one in the input circuit (IC3(a), IC3(b) and IC4).

Most of the work is done by IC1 and IC2. These two chips – MN3102 and MN3207 – are designed to be used together, and will provide delay times from 2.5ms to 50ms or so. The 3102 contains a timing circuit that provides the two-phase clock signal required to drive the 3207. It also produces the correct gate supply voltage for the 3207 which is connected to the Vgg input (Fig. 2.7).

Signals from the preamp circuitry are fed into IC2 at pin 3. The output from the delay line is via pins 7 and 8, which are biased by R2 and R3. VR2 is connected across the two outputs and provides a single balanced output. IC1 has three direct connections to IC2. These carry the two clock signals and the gate voltage (Vgg). The clock frequency of IC1 – and the overall delay time of the circuit – is set by C1 and VR1. R1 acts as an end stop for VR1 as the resistance across pins 5 and 7 should not be less than 5k. Varying the value of VR1 will change the delay time given by IC2. This example has C1 as 220pF, but

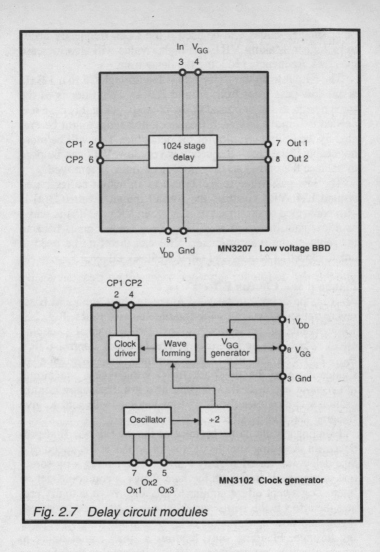

Fig. 2.7 Delay circuit modules

other smaller values can be used if the clock frequency needs to be higher. Making VR1 of a higher value will also increase the clock frequency, reducing the delay time.

The output from the delay line is fed through C5 to a 12kHz active low-pass filter built around IC3(a). This filter is of the same design as the one used in the preamp, but in this case it is needed to remove any high frequency noise that might be created by the timing circuitry of the delay line. This will be more noticeable if the clock frequency is very low. VR2 can be used to balance the output so that most clock noise is removed.

The low-pass filter feeds signals to an output buffer based around IC4. VR4 controls the overall output level. IC3(a) is also connected to the input of IC3(b) via VR3. IC3(b) is wired as a low gain inverting amplifier which feeds signals back to the input of the preamp/mixer. VR3 can therefore be used to create repeating echoes and other feedback effects.

Flanging and Chorus Effects

As it is, the delay can be used to create short echo and basic reverberation effects. Moving the time control (VR1, Fig. 2.5) while signals are present will give a sort of manual sweeping effect, which can be interesting. The feedback control (VR3, Fig. 2.5) can be used to accentuate the resonance of signals close to the feedback limit. What makes the circuit much more useful is the addition of a low frequency control oscillator to modulate the delay time automatically and so give flanging and chorus effects.

Flanging got its name because of the way it was first produced. In recording studios, it was found that if the speed of a tape delay was varied slightly while it was running – by someone putting their finger on the tape flange – you could get an interesting swept effect similar to phasing. What actually creates the effect is the slight variable de-tuning caused by speeding up and slowing down the delay time while a signal is passing through. Flanging only requires a small signal delay to sound effective, no more than 10 or 15ms, and is therefore an ideal effect to make with an analogue delay line.

The chorus effect is similar to flanging except that it is often more subtle, and simply used to beef up an instrument by creating a richer texture of sound, as if two or more instruments were playing the same thing at the same time. This is achieved in the same way as flanging, by slight de-tuning of a signal, except that in chorus there is usually little or no resonant feedback.

Figure 2.6 shows a simple low frequency triangle wave oscillator which can be connected to the clock circuit of the MN3102. With the component values shown, the frequency of the oscillator may be varied from around 0.5Hz to 5Hz or so. With this range a good degree of variation may be achieved, from very slow swept effects to fast vibrato.

The oscillator is a standard design based around two op-amps – virtually any general purpose types will do – though the PCB layout shown (Figs 2.12 and 2.13) uses the pin layout for the TL072, which is a dual device. The speed of the oscillator is controlled by VR1, with the output being taken from IC1(a). If a depth control is required, you can connect a 10k pot in series with R5.

The switch S1 is included to allow the oscillator to be disconnected from the clock circuit, at the same time as reconnecting a manual delay control (VR2). This means that the delay can be used with or without the LFO, and allows it to produce all the usual short echo effects as well as the ones that involve modulation. If the manual control is not required, the oscillator can be connected as shown in Figure 2.14.

PCB layouts for the input circuitry, the delay line and the control oscillator are shown in Figures 2.8 to 2.13.

Components for Analogue Delay Input Circuitry (Fig. 2.4)

Resistors (all 0.25 watt 5% carbon film)

R1, R2, R3, R4	47k (4 off)
R5, R6	10k (2 off)
R7	1k
VR1	470k

Capacitors

C1, C2, C3, C4, C5, C8	1µF 16V electrolytic (6 off)
C6, C7	1nF polyester
C9	100µF 16V electrolytic
C10	100nF polyester

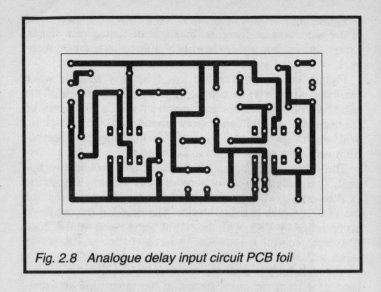

Fig. 2.8 Analogue delay input circuit PCB foil

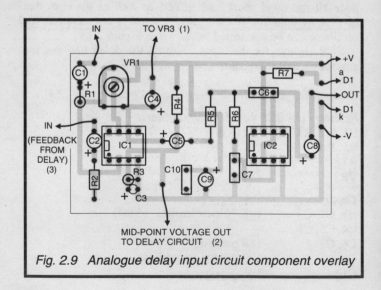

Fig. 2.9 Analogue delay input circuit component overlay

48

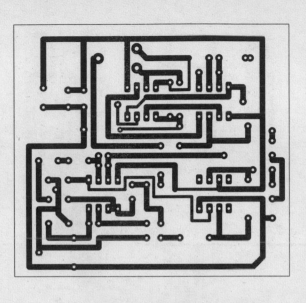

Fig. 2.10   Analogue delay PCB foil

Semiconductors
IC1, IC2   TL071
D1   3mm low current LED

Components for Analogue Delay Line (Fig. 2.5)

Resistors (all 0.25 watt 5% carbon film)
R1   5k6
R2, R3   100k (2 off)
R4, R5, R6   12k (3 off)
R7   15k
R8   1k
R9   10k
VR1   100k lin pot
VR2   10k preset

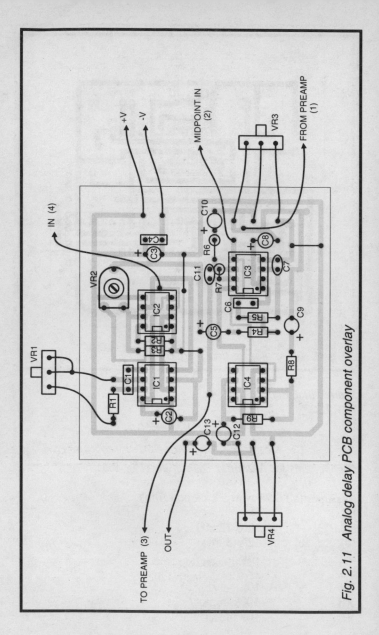

Fig. 2.11 Analog delay PCB component overlay

Fig. 2.12 Modulation oscillator PCB foil

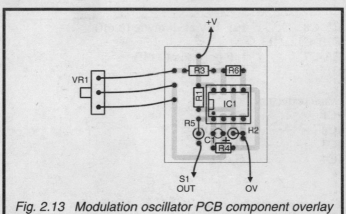

Fig. 2.13 Modulation oscillator PCB component overlay

| VR3 | 25k lin pot |
| VR4 | 1k log pot |

Capacitors

C1	220pF ceramic
C2	2μ2 16V electrolytic
C3	100μF 16V electrolytic
C4	100nF polyester

51

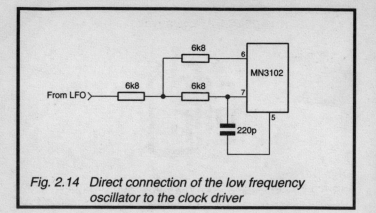

Fig. 2.14   Direct connection of the low frequency oscillator to the clock driver

C5, C8, C9, C10, C12, C13	1µF 16V electrolytic (6 off)
C6, C7	1nF polyester (2 off)
C11	39pF

Semiconductors
IC1	MN3102
IC2	MN3207
IC3	TL072
IC4	TL071

Components for Analogue Delay Line Modulation Oscillator (Fig. 2.6)

Resistors (all 0.25 watt 5% carbon film)
R1	10k
R2	5k6
R3	1k
R4	100k
R5	6k8
R6	470k
R7, R8	6k8
VR1, VR2	6k8 (2 off)

Capacitors
C1   22µF 16V electrolytic

Semiconductors
IC1   TL072

Miscellaneous
S1   DPDT switch

Digital Delay
For long delays in high quality audio and recording, digital
delay lines are used almost exclusively. As you would expect,
digital delays can be extremely complex pieces of equipment to
build, especially if you have to construct all the control circuitry and A/D – D/A converters from scratch. Luckily there are
now a number of reasonably cheap ICs available that have most
of the necessary building blocks to make a usable system, with
only a relatively small amount of extra circuitry. This is great if
you just want to experiment but don't want to go to the trouble
of building anything too complex.

The digital delay circuit shown in Figure 2.15 can produce
surprisingly good results if set up carefully and will give delay
times of up to 200ms with a 64K RAM or 800ms with a 256K
RAM.

Like the other effects circuits in this book, the digital delay
is really intended to be directly connected to the output of an
electric guitar or other electronic instrument, but may equally
well end up being used with higher level signals in, say, an
auxiliary effects loop in a PA or sound system. Because of the
fairly wide range of input levels it may be expected to handle,
input signals are channelled through a variable gain preamp
before they get to the input of the delay line.

The input preamp is built around an ultra low noise NE5534.
Using this IC as the first stage amplifier will help reduce overall noise throughout the system, though a cheaper TL071, or
any other general purpose op-amp, could be used.

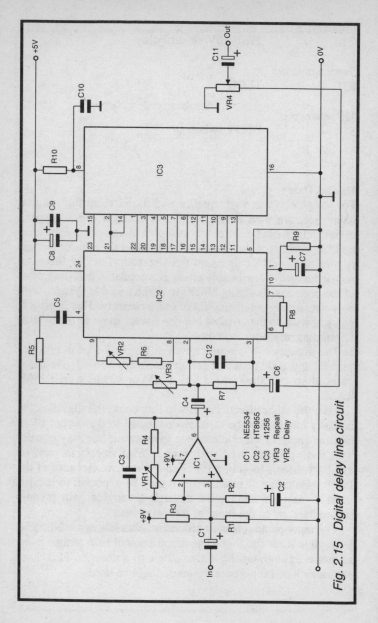

Fig. 2.15 Digital delay line circuit

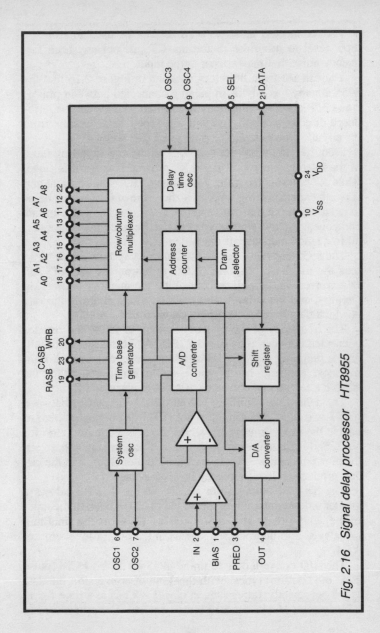

Fig. 2.16 Signal delay processor HT8955

55

VR1 connected in series with R4 can be used to trim the input level to minimise distortion. C3 cuts out any high frequency noise that may appear at the input.

You can see from the block diagram in Figure 2.16 that the 8955 already has a built-in preamp connected between pins 1, 2 and 3. If absolute simplicity is required, signals can be introduced directly to pin 2, but you can expect better results from the circuit if the external preamp is used as well.

From IC1, signals enter the 8955 via the non-inverting input of the internal preamp. C7 and R9 provide bias for this stage, while R7 controls the gain. The value of R7 is not critical and is worth experimenting with, as is the value of C12 which helps to reduce some of the system noise. The higher the value of this component the more noise you cut out, but the lower the overall frequency response of the system.

The 8955 has two internal oscillators. A system oscillator to feed the timebase generator which synchronises the A/D and D/A converters, as well as controlling the memory addressing circuitry, and the delay time oscillator which controls the rate at which data is fed to and from the memory.

The frequency of the system oscillator is set by the resistor connected between pins 6 and 7 (R8). A 5k6 resistor here will give a sampling rate of 25kHz, which seems to be about right for most applications. If you want to experiment with the sample rate you can connect a 10k pot in place of R8.

The delay time oscillator is controlled by a resistor between pins 8 and 9. In this circuit, a pot (VR2) is connected here to enable the delay time to be varied. R6 acts as an end stop for VR2, and is quite important, because if the resistance between the pins falls below 100k or so, the oscillator stops, and the circuit produces a low frequency howling noise.

The delayed output from IC2 is via pin 4. VR3 allows a greater or lesser amount of the output to be fed back to the input of the delay line to give repeat echoes. C6 takes the final mix of delayed and unprocessed signals to the output level control VR4.

The A/D converters used in the 8955 are 10 bit PCM (pulse code modulation) types. With this kind of conversion the data is fed out serially, rather than in blocks – 8 bits at a time for an 8 bit system, 16 bits for a 16 bit system, etc. The processor can be used with either a 4164 or a 41256 DRAM chip. Both these ICs have the same pinouts so they can be changed round without difficulty as long as an IC socket is used. The only thing you should remember is that the chip select pin on the 8955 (pin 5) needs to be connected to ground if a 41256 is used, and left open for the smaller 4164. The PCB layout shown here (Figs 2.17 and 2.18) has pin 5 of IC1 connected to ground.

Both the 8955 and the 4164/256 require a 5V supply, so if the circuit needs to be used with a higher voltage, 9V from a PP3 battery for instance, the circuit shown in Figure 2.19

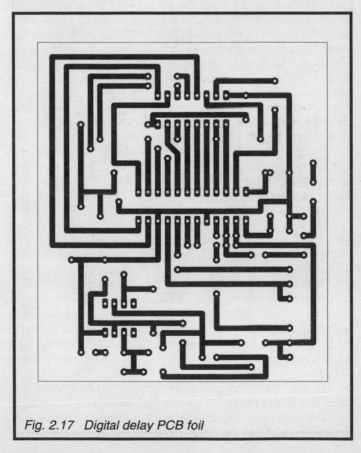

Fig. 2.17   Digital delay PCB foil

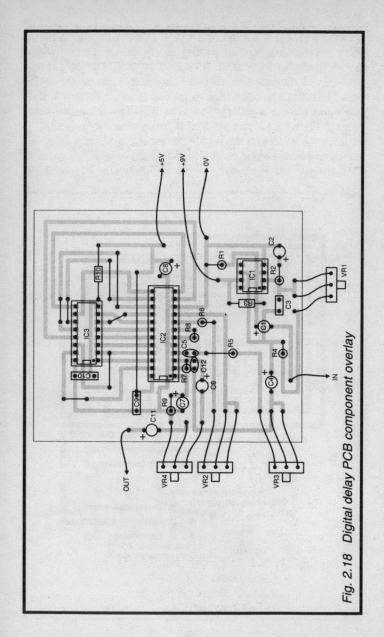

Fig. 2.18 Digital delay PCB component overlay

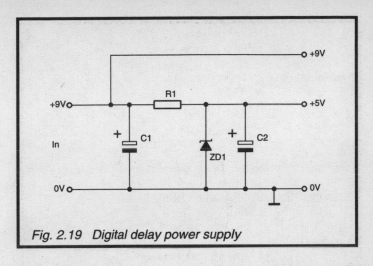

Fig. 2.19 Digital delay power supply

should be included to drop the voltage down to a safe level. IC1 can be connected straight to the 9V rail as it has a higher supply voltage range (±3V to ±20V).

Components for Digital Delay Line (Fig. 2.15)

Resistors (all 0.25 watt 5% carbon film)
R1, R3, R7	100k (3 off)
R2, R4	2k2 (2 off)
R5	680k
R6	180k
R8	5k6
R9	560k
R10	4R7
VR1	100k log pot
VR2, VR3	470k lin pot (2 off)
VR4	470k log pot

Capacitors
C1, C4, C6, C11	1µF 16V electrolytic (4 off)
C2	4µ7 electrolytic 16V
C3	220pF ceramic
C5	10nF polyester

C7, C8	100µF 16V electrolytic (2 off)
C9, C10	100nF polyester (2 off)
C12	330pF ceramic

Semiconductors
IC1	NE5534
IC2	HT8955
IC3	41256

Components for Digital Delay Line Power Supply (Fig. 2.19)

Resistors (0.25 watt 5% carbon film)
| R1 | 150R |

Capacitors
| C1 | 470µF 16V electrolytic |
| C2 | 47µF 16V electrolytic |

Semiconductors
| ZD1 | BZX61 5.1V zener diode |

Noise Reduction Circuit

Because of the basic nature of the digital delay described here, you may find that the levels of system noise produced need reducing to give a better signal quality. Figure 2.20, and the PCB layouts in Figures 2.21 and 2.22, show a simple noise gate that can be connected to the output of the unit to cut down on the unwanted background noise that builds up when there is no signal present to mask it. It is based around an NE571 compander wired as a signal compressor followed by a complementary expander. The level at which the gate starts to cut off is set by VR1. S1, connected in series with VR1, can be used to turn the gate on and off. With S1 open the circuit has no effect on signals passing through it.

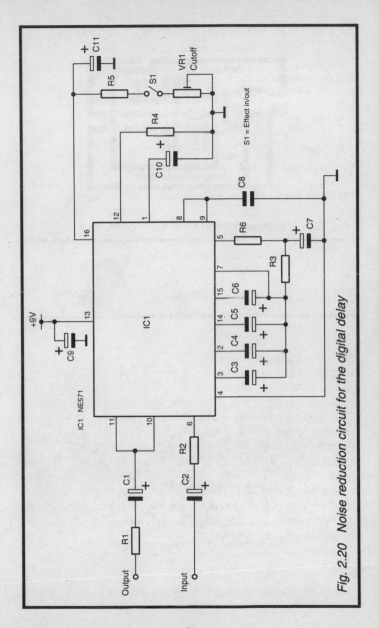

Fig. 2.20 Noise reduction circuit for the digital delay

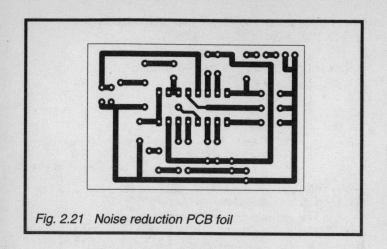

Fig. 2.21 Noise reduction PCB foil

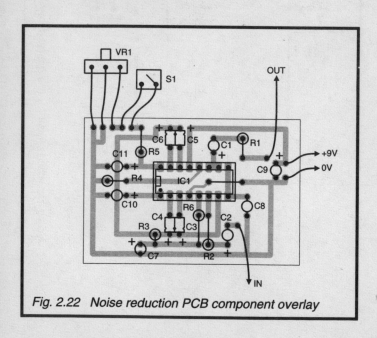

Fig. 2.22 Noise reduction PCB component overlay

Components for Digital Delay Line Noise Reduction Circuit (Fig. 2.20)

Resistors (all 0.25 watt 5% carbon film)
R1	100R
R2	470R
R3, R6	15k (2 off)
R4	47k
R5	100k
VR1	2M2 lin preset

Capacitors
C1, C2, C3, C4, C5, C6, C7, C10, C11	1µF tantalum bead 16V (9 off)
C8	47nF polyester
C9	100µF 16V electrolytic

Semiconductor
IC1	NE571 compander

Chapter 3

HEADPHONE PRACTICE AMPLIFIER

A good quality practice amplifier is a really useful piece of equipment, especially if your main amplifier is large and awkward to set up. What is required from a practice amplifier is a decent sound at a low volume, along with, say, more than one channel so that you can plug a couple of instruments in if you want to practise with someone else.

Many of the cheaper models, which are often bought as a first guitar amplifier, sound really bad even if you play a good instrument through them, which can be discouraging, and is often due partly to poor speaker and case construction. It is also quite common to see two or three input sockets, only to find that they are not in fact independent channels, but simply connected to a single preamp. This may not matter too much for lone practice, but can cause trouble if you double up with an instrument that sounds radically different from your own. For a more practical and usable amp you really need separate channels with independent tone controls, so that a reasonable sound balance can be obtained no matter what you plug in.

The practice amplifier shown here will drive two pairs of high quality headphones, and should be useful in many situations where a normal amp might be awkward to use. Getting a good sound from headphones is easier than driving speakers, and also does away with the need for a large case and power supply. The input section does, however, have an auxiliary output to enable it to be connected to a larger power-amp and speakers if required.

The input section has three independent channels and will give high quality results even at low volumes. This circuitry could also be used on its own as a high quality mixer. The two headphone outputs have their own level controls to make things easier if two people want to practise together.

Input Circuit

The input circuitry shown in Figure 3.1 is built around three of the four low noise op-amps in a TL074. The preamps are wired

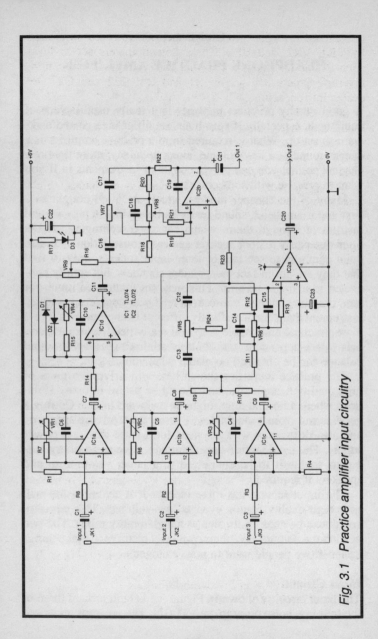

Fig. 3.1 Practice amplifier input circuitry

in standard inverting mode with the gain for each controlled by VR1, VR2, and VR3. These potentiometers act as level controls for the inputs. The mid rail voltages for the non-inverting inputs are set by R1 and R4. C22 and C23 are decoupling capacitors.

Channel 1 is intended to be the guitar channel, and has a higher gain than channels 2 and 3. This is so that it can be used to create over-driven sounds if required. Channels 2 and 3 can be fed with signals from instruments or mics, as well as high level signals from tape recorders, etc.

The output from the channel 1 preamp is fed into a simple distortion circuit like the one described earlier (Fig. 1.2). This is constructed around the remaining op-amp in IC1, and has variable effect and mix controls (VR4 and VR9). The output from the wiper of VR9 will be a progressive mix between the clean output from IC1a and the distortion coming from IC1d. Maximum distortion will be obtained if VR1 and VR4 are set to give the highest gain. Distortion will also be created in the following stage which is an active tone control, built round the feedback path of IC2b.

This is a standard Baxendall arrangement with high and low-pass filters in parallel. VR7 controls the treble and VR8 controls the bass. C19 gets rid of high frequency noise. Capacitors C4, C5 and C6 perform the same function for the input pre-amps.

The outputs from channels 2 and 3 are fed into an identical tone control circuit via C8 and C9, with VR5 controlling the treble and VR6 the bass frequencies.

The preamp circuitry has two outputs. Output one is channel one on its own. The other output is channel 2 and channel 3 together. You may like to have extra level controls connected across the channel outputs, especially if IC1a and IC1d are going to be used to overdrive the channel 1 tone circuit. For simplicity they have not been included in this circuit.

Components for Practice Amplifier Input Circuitry (Fig. 3.1)

Resistors (all 0.25 watt 5% carbon film)
R1, R4, R7, R8   47k (4 off)
R2, R6   10k (2 off)

R3, R5, R9,	1k (5 off)
R10, R16	
R11, R12, R13,	5k6 (6 off)
R18, R20, R21	
R19, R24	39k (2 off)
R14, R15	22k (2 off)
R17	390R
R22, R23	470R (2 off)
VR1	1M log pot
VR2	100k log pot
VR3	10k log pot
VR4	1M log pot
VR5–VR8	100k lin pots (4 off)
VR9	1M lin pot

Capacitors

C1, C2, C3, C7,	1µF 16V electrolytic (9 off)
C8, C9, C11,	
C20, C21	
C4, C5, C6,	180pF ceramic (4 off)
C10	
C12, C13, C16,	1nF polyester (4 off)
C17	
C14, C18	100nF polyester
C15, C19	39pF ceramic (2 off)
C22	100µF 16V electrolytic
C23	10µF 16V electrolytic

Semiconductors

IC1	TL074 quad op-amp
IC2	TL072 dual op-amp
D1, D2	OA91 germanium diode (2 off)
D3	LED

Miscellaneous

| JK1 – JK3 | ¼ inch mono jack sockets (3 off) |

Twin Headphone Power-amp

The circuit shown in Figure 3.2 is a stereo power-amp based round a TDA2822. This IC is really intended to drive one pair

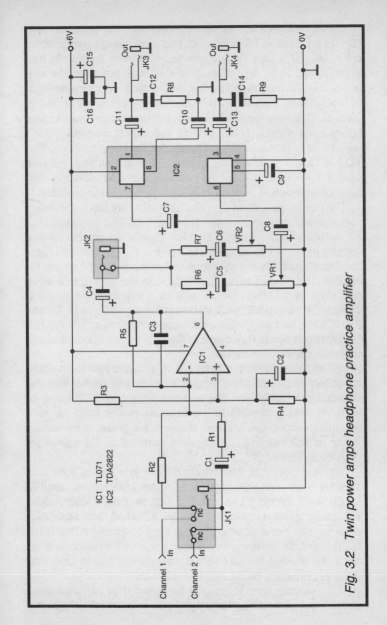

Fig. 3.2 Twin power amps headphone practice amplifier

IC1 TL071
IC2 TDA2822

of stereo headphones, in applications such as portable tape players and radios. Normally, its two power-amps would drive either side of a pair of headphones separately to enable true stereo sound to be reproduced. In this case, however, the two power-amps are arranged so that they each drive a separate pair of headphones, with the two headphone elements connected in parallel. This may seem a little odd, but in practice it works fine because the signals from guitars and basses normally don't need to be in true stereo – certainly not for just practising. The TDA2822 will handle loads from 4 – 32R and supplies ranging from 1.8 – 15V. A normal pair of 32R stereo headphones will have a resistance of around 16R when connected in parallel.

The two outputs from the preamp section are fed to the headphone power amp via R1 and R2 (Fig. 3.2). JK1 is included as an auxiliary input which enables signals to be introduced directly to the power-amp. When a jack is plugged into JK1, the two input channels are disconnected and signals fed in via C1 and R1. JK1 should be a type of jack socket having two separate SPST or a DPDT switch built in. It can be omitted if it is unlikely to be needed, with the inputs going straight to R1 and R2. IC1 is wired as a unity gain amplifier which mixes the two channels and sends its output to the two volume pots connected to the power-amp inputs.

JK2 enables the output from IC1 to be connected to an external power-amp or mixer. Plugging a jack to this socket also disconnects the headphone power-amps. This output can also be used for taking signals to an external power amp, or as a recording output. Once again, if this is not going to be needed it can be left out and the negative terminal of C4 connected directly to R6 and R7.

You may feel that three channels and two sets of tone controls are more than you require. To make a more basic amplifier, the input circuitry can be simplified to make a single channel circuit by leaving out IC1b, IC1c, IC2a and their associated components. For a double channel amp leave out IC1a, IC1d, IC2b and their components. If tone controls and distortion are not required, signals can be taken straight to a power amp from the input preamps (IC1a, IC1b and IC1c).

If the practice amp is going to be powered by batteries, these should be 4 or 5 of the large 1.5V types. It is probably best to avoid using small batteries such as 9V PP3s unless the amp needs to be really small, because they may not last too long with regular use. Type C or D cells will probably give the most economical results. Suitable holders are easily obtained. The circuit will operate over quite a wide range of voltages, the TL074 and TL072 will work from ±2V to ±18V, while the TDA2822 has a supply range of 1.8 – 15V. So any voltage around 6 – 12V is fine.

When constructing the amplifier remember to keep all the wiring as short as you can, to cut down on noise. If possible use a metal case and have one central point as 'earth' – a large solder tag connected to the case will do. This will help to avoid trouble with earth loops if the amp is connected to other equipment. It is also a good idea to screen the cables that connect the potentiometers and earth their cases.

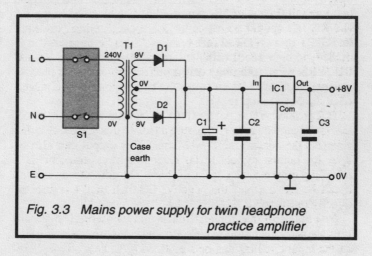

Fig. 3.3 Mains power supply for twin headphone practice amplifier

If mains power is required, the circuit shown in Figure 3.3 can be used. This is a simple arrangement utilising a centre tapped 9–0–9V transformer and will give an output of 8V using the voltage regulator specified. The regulator is not critical and can be any type that gives a voltage within the required range. The smoothing capacitor C1 should be as large as possible, at least 2200µF, and be rated at 25V or more. This circuit will supply most of the other effects circuits shown in this book, as well as manufactured effects pedals, though if you are going to use it for this type of application, it is more important to include the voltage regulator. Almost all manufactured effects pedals will require a 9V supply, so choose a regulator which gives this voltage.

Once mains voltages are involved, special care must be taken to ensure the correct safety precautions are observed in construction. Always use an earthed metal case, and make sure that any parts of the circuit that carry mains voltage are adequately insulated.

Components for Twin Headphone Practice Amplifier
Power Amps (Fig. 3.2)

Resistors (all 0.25 watt 5% carbon film)
R1 – R5	47k (5 off)
R6, R7	560k (2 off)
R8, R9	1R (2 off)
VR1, VR2	100k log pots (2 off)

Capacitors
C1, C4, C5, C6, C7, C8	1µF electrolytic (6 off)
C2	10µF 16V electrolytic
C3	38pF ceramic
C9, C10, C15	100µF 16V electrolytic (3 off)
C11, C13	470µF 16V electrolytic (2 off)
C12, C14	220nF polyester (2 off)
C16	100nF polyester

Semiconductors
IC1	TL071
IC2	TDA2822

Miscellaneous
JK1	mono ¼ inch jack socket with two change-over or SPST internal switches
JK2	mono ¼ inch jack socket with internal SPST switch
JK3, JK4	stereo 2.5mm jack sockets (2 off)

Components for Twin Headphone Practice Amp Power Supply (Fig. 3.3)

Transformer
T1   9–0–9V transformer

Capacitors
C1   2200µF 25V electrolytic
C2, C3   220nF polyester

Semiconductors
D1, D2   1N4001 (2 off)
IC1   UA7808

Miscellaneous
S1   DPST mains rated switch

Chapter 4

ELECTRONIC CONTROL

The more control options you build into an electric guitar or bass, the more cluttered the front of the instrument can become. Even if you use combined potentiometer/switches (pull-pots) to add functions, you can still end up needing more switches for some combinations. If an instrument has limited space for controls, or maybe wouldn't suit a lot of switches, a way round the problem is to have some form of electronic control so that one or two switches can be made to govern the operation of a large number of circuits. There have been a few commercially produced and experimental guitars that included this type of control, but they have tended not to be very popular, probably because they were seen as a bit gimmicky or overly complicated. One design even had a memory for storing the positions of the volume and tone controls, as well as the pickup settings for about 100 sounds, which seems a bit excessive.

The circuits shown in Figures 4.1 and 4.2 make up a relatively simple electronic switching set up which can control the pickup selection, coil taps, phase reversal and active tone on/bypass, for a three pickup guitar, but only needs two SPST switches.

It was originally designed for a guitar that had to be as uncluttered by controls as possible, yet as it was intended for studio work, needed to be able to produce the whole range of standard guitar sounds.

In the set up shown here, the first pickup is a humbucker (twin coils) and the other two are single coil. You will see from the block diagram in Figure 4.3 that the circuit could easily be expanded or simplified to switch other pickup arrangements, depending on the number of relays and switches you want to use. Space for the circuit board may be a problem in guitars with small control routs, but if you are building an instrument from scratch this can be taken into account. The prototype was crammed onto a PCB that measured about 5 × 4 cm and contained all the relays and switching transistors as well as a control oscillator for IC2 (Fig. 4.10).

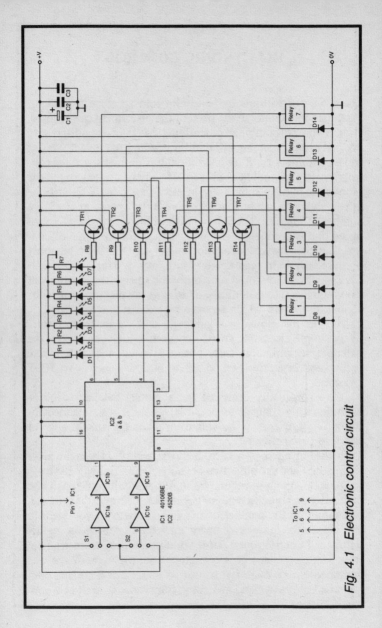

Fig. 4.1 Electronic control circuit

76

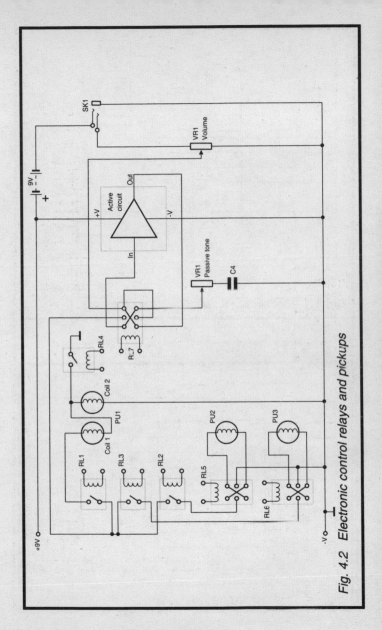

Fig. 4.2 Electronic control relays and pickups

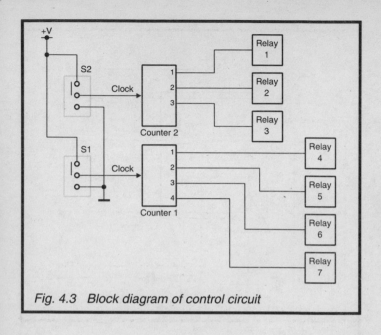

Fig. 4.3 Block diagram of control circuit

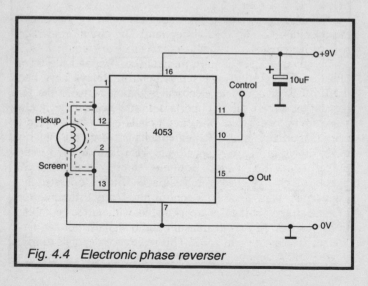

Fig. 4.4 Electronic phase reverser

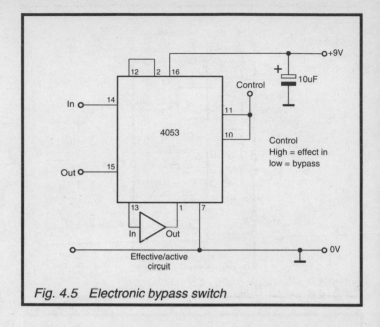

Fig. 4.5   Electronic bypass switch

Although it may look a little complicated for a guitar circuit, the operation is fairly straightforward. The circuit consists of two main parts – a manually operated binary counter (IC2) which governs a set of ultra miniature relays, and the actual pickup circuitry which the relays control. Relays have been used to ensure complete electrical isolation between the two parts of the circuit, this is important if problems with switching noise are to be avoided. The circuit could easily be adapted to operate the electronic switching circuits based on transmission gates shown in Figure 4.4 and 4.5. These use a 4053 multiplexer (Fig. 4.6) which contains three independent bi-directional change-over switches. Each switch is operated by a high or low logic level on a control pin. Many different types of analogue switching ICs are available, with various combinations of gates. Most will transmit audio signals, but can have 'on'resistances of up to 250R. This resistance depends to some degree on the supply voltage used. The higher the supply, the lower the 'on' resistance.

79

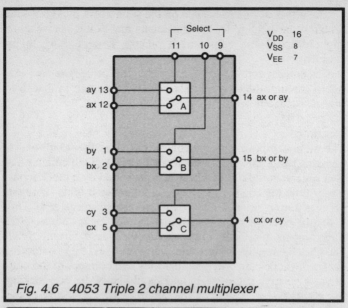

Fig. 4.6 4053 Triple 2 channel multiplexer

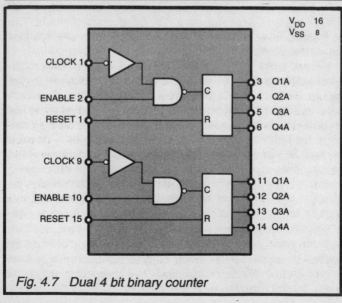

Fig. 4.7 Dual 4 bit binary counter

The effect of this resistance on the sound of a pickup would probably be negligible, but musicians are fickle, and even a slight drop in the output of a pickup is something to be avoided.

Mechanical relays were chosen for the prototype for simplicity, though they have another small advantage in that their 'on' resistance is virtually 0.

Counter

The main component in the control circuit is the 4520, which contains two 4 bit binary counters (Fig. 4.7). Each counter has four separate outputs, and these are controlled by a clock input. Every time the counter receives a clock pulse it adds '1' to the counter until it reaches '1111' when it resets back to zero. This gives 16 possible output combinations for each counter. The clock inputs for the counters are controlled by mini SPST switches S1 and S2. S1 runs the counter (a), and S2 counter (b).

The switches are wired so that they can connect to the negative or positive supply rails, and should be of the non-locking variety to make sequencing the counter easier. Because of the high gain of the counters input circuitry, the clock switch always needs to be connected to one or other supply rails. This will improve the stability of the circuit and stop any spurious pulses that might occur if the input was left floating.

Operating S1 or S2 gives a logic high or low input to the inverters IC1(a) and IC1(c). These inverters are Schmitt trigger types and ensure that a pulse is registered every time the switch is operated. The switches could be connected directly to the clock inputs, but this arrangement was found to be a little erratic, and might be unreliable, especially if the switch contacts ever became worn or dirty. The Schmitt trigger inverters give a sharply defined output even if the input to them is a bit ragged.

The inverter IC1(a) is followed by IC1(b) which restores the correct logic level and feeds the clock input of the counter IC2(a). IC1(c) and IC1(d) work in the same way feeding IC2(b). The outputs from the two counters are connected to the switching transistors TR1 – TR7. These in turn operate the miniature relays 1 – 7 which control the pickup selection. IC2(b) controls the first three relays, which select pickups 1, 2 and 3, IC2(a) controls the other four, and operates the coil tap for pickup 1, phase reversal for pickups 2 and 3, and the active tone control on/off.

Operation

A clock pulse created by pressing S2 will turn on the first relay and connect pickup one to the output, a second pulse turns relay one off and relay two on, connecting the middle pickup to the output. A third pulse turns both relays on, and a fourth has the third pickup connected on its own. This continues through every combination of the three switches until the counter reaches 8 or '111' in binary. The 9th pulse sets all the outputs back to zero.

The counter IC2(a) uses all four of its outputs, and these operate the other switches that the guitar circuit uses. The first one controls a SPST relay RL4 for the coil tap in pickup 1. The next two control DPDT relays (RL5 and RL6) for reversing the phase of pickups 1 and 2. The active tone control is switched in and out by a DPDT relay (RL7) on the fourth output.

The table in Figure 4.8 gives the full range of switching options available with the circuit.

The relays used in the controller are ultra miniature low power types, which makes them very small – about the size of a TO5 transistor for the SPST relays. They all have diodes connected across them to stop any induced high voltage spikes from damaging the circuit when they turn off.

The capacitors C2 and C3 help decouple the supply rails and should be mounted as close to the ICs as possible. The input circuitry of the CMOS chips has a very high gain and will tend to oscillate if it gets the chance.

Guitar Circuit

On the pickup side of the relays the guitar circuitry is fairly straightforward. The setup has three pickups. PU1 is a humbucker switched by RL1, with a coil tap controlled by RL4. Both of these relays are single pole. RL4 acts by shorting the second coil in pickup 1 to earth. If you are using a twin coil pickup that only has adjustable pole pieces for one coil, you should have the coil tap shorting the non-adjustable coil.

Pickup 1	Pickup 2	Pickup 3
0	0	0
1	0	0
0	1	0
1	1	0
0	0	1
1	0	1
0	1	1
1	1	1

1 = on
0 = off

Switching options for counter 1

P1 Tap	P2 Phase	P3 Phase	Active
0	0	0	0
1	0	0	0
0	1	0	0
1	1	0	0
0	0	1	0
1	0	1	0
0	1	1	0
1	1	1	0
0	0	0	1
1	0	0	1
0	1	0	1
1	1	0	1
0	0	1	1
1	0	1	1
0	1	1	1
1	1	1	1

Switching options for counter 2

Fig. 4.8 Switching options for counters

The most effective position for a single humbucker would probably be close to the bridge, but it is really up to you how the pickups are arranged. PU2 and PU3 are single coil units for the mid and neck positions. These pickups both have two relays

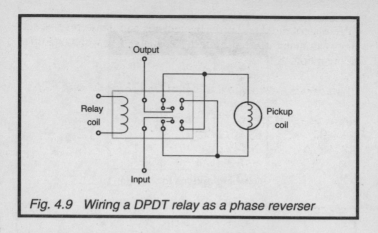

Fig. 4.9   Wiring a DPDT relay as a phase reverser

controlling them. RL2 and RL3 switch them in and out, and are single pole types, while RL5 and RL6 are double pole, wired as phase reversers. You should remember to use twin core screened wire for these pickups, as either side of the coil could be connected to the output of the phase relay, depending on how it is set. Figure 4.9 shows how to connect the relays for the phase reverse.

The active tone circuit is controlled by RL7, which acts in the same way as a normal by-pass switch, taking the output from the pickups directly to the volume pot via a passive tone control made up of C4 and VR1. When the relay is switched in, VR1 is disconnected, and the signal passes through the active circuit before reaching the volume control. Any active tone circuit may be used for this set up, and if you make VR1 a stereo pot you can have both the active and passive tone operated by the same control knob.

LEDs
Because there are so many switching combinations available with this circuit, it might be helpful to include the LEDs D1 – D7 mounted somewhere on the guitar. These are optional but make the finding of regularly used pickup and switch settings much simpler. If you use ultra miniature LEDs they can be made quite innocuous, even on the front of a guitar. Having

different coloured LEDs for the pickups and phase reverse settings can make it even easier to see at a glance which set up is in operation.

Components for Electronic Control Unit (Figs 4.1 and 4.2)

Resistors (all 0.25 watt 5% carbon film)
R1 – R7   680R (7 off)
R8 – R14   1k8 (7 off)
VR1   470k lin pot
VR2   470k log pot

Capacitors
C1   100µF 16V electrolytic
C2, C3   100nF polyester

Semiconductors
IC1   40106
IC2   4520
TR1 – TR7   BC 142 (7 off)
D1 – D7   ultra miniature LEDs (7 off)
D8 – D14   1N4148 (7 off)

Miscellaneous
Relays 1, 2, 3, 4 ultra miniature single pole (4 off)
Relays 5, 6, 7   ultra miniature double pole (3 off)
S1, S2   SPST non-locking switch (2 off)

Control Oscillator
A useful refinement that can be made to the control circuit is the inclusion of a clocking oscillator to automatically sequence the outputs of the counters. One oscillator can be made to operate both counter circuits separately by using a SPDT switch to connect its output to either clock input (Fig. 4.10). The oscillator runs all the time but its output is only connected when the switch is pressed. If you use a non-locking centre off switch you can control the pickup counter with it pressed one way, and the phase reverse/coil tap counter with it pressed the other way.

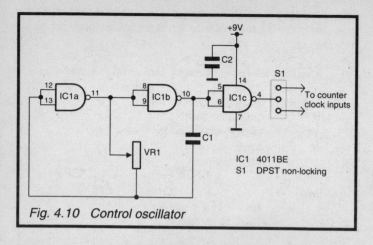

Fig. 4.10   Control oscillator

The oscillator is a conventional square wave type based on a 4011 quad NAND gate, and can trigger the clock inputs of the counters directly, replacing the inverters. One of the four gates, IC1(c) is connected to act as a buffer for the output. The frequency of operation depends on the value of the capacitor C1, and the preset VR1. With the values shown here the oscillator will have a minimum frequency of around 2Hz, which is slow enough to enable the changing settings to be observed. The output from the oscillator is wired to the middle centre off terminal of a selector switch, and this enables the signal to be channelled directly to either of the counters' clock inputs. As with all CMOS ICs you should connect unused terminals to one of the supply rails.

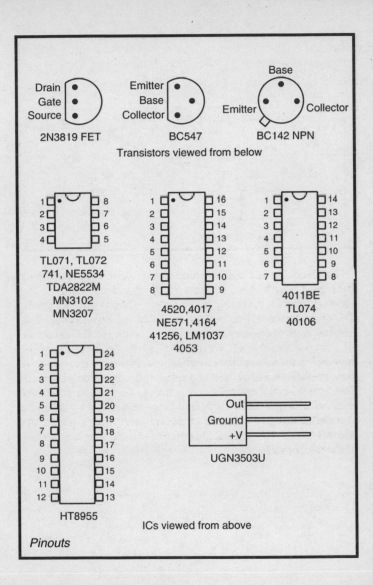

Drain
Gate
Source

2N3819 FET

Emitter
Base
Collector

BC547

Base

Emitter
Collector

BC142 NPN

Transistors viewed from below

TL071, TL072
741, NE5534
TDA2822M
MN3102
MN3207

4520, 4017
NE571, 4164
41256, LM1037
4053

4011BE
TL074
40106

HT8955

Out
Ground
+V

UGN3503U

ICs viewed from above

Pinouts